Black BEAUTY

by Anna Sewell   retold by L. L. Owens   illustrated by Jennifer Tanner

Librarian Reviewer
Allyson A.W. Lyga MS
Library Media/Graphic Novel Consultant

Reading Consultant
Mark DeYoung
Classroom Teacher

www.raintreepublishers.co.uk
Visit our website to find out
more information about
Raintree books.

To order:
☎ Phone +44 (0) 1865 888066
🖷 Fax +44 (0) 1865 314091
💻 Visit www.raintreepublishers.co.uk

Raintree is an imprint of Capstone Global Library Limited, a company incorporated in
England and Wales having its registered office at 7 Pilgrim Street, London, EC4V 6LB –
Registered company number: 6695582

"Raintree" is a registered trademark of Pearson Education Limited, under licence to
Capstone Global Library Limited

Text © Stone Arch Books, 2009
First published by Stone Arch Books in 2007
First published in hardback in the United Kingdom in 2009
First published in paperback in the United Kingdom in 2010
The moral rights of the proprietor have been asserted.

Art Director: Heather Kindseth
Graphic Designer: Kay Fraser
Edited in the UK by Laura Knowles
Printed and bound in China by Leo Paper Products Ltd

ISBN 978-1406212464 (hardback)
13 12 11 10 09
10 9 8 7 6 5 4 3 2 1

ISBN 978-1406213485 (paperback)
14 13 12 11 10
10 9 8 7 6 5 4 3 2 1

British Library Cataloguing in Publication Data
Owens, L. L.
Black Beauty. -- (Graphic revolve)
741.5-dc22
A full catalogue record for this book is available from the British Library.

Table of CONTENTS

Duchess

Black Beauty's mother

Ginger

Black Beauty's carriage partner
and friend at Birtwick Park.

Jerry

A cabbie who owns
Black Beauty

Black Beauty

Joe Green
A stable boy

Merrylegs
Black Beauty's stable mate
and friend at Birtwick Park.

My first home was with Farmer Grey. I can still picture his pleasant meadow and the pond of clear water.

I lived there with my mother, Duchess. She was proud that we came from a long line of fine horses.

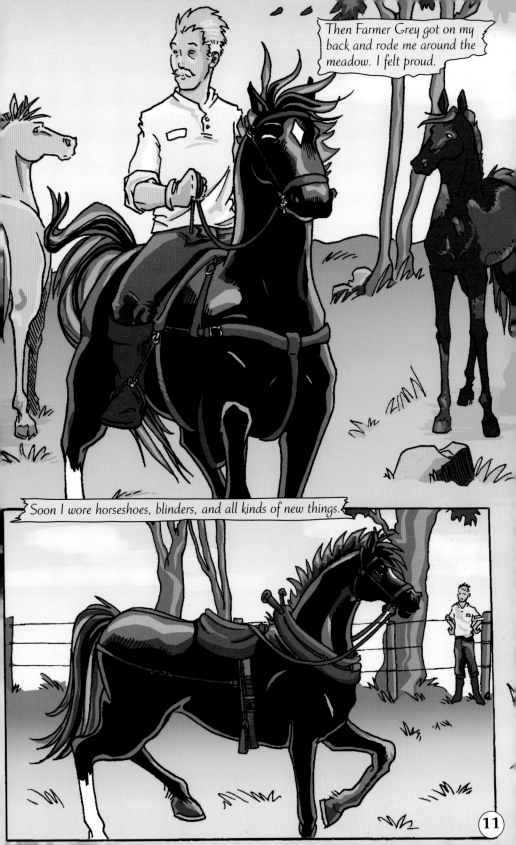

As part of my training, I stayed two weeks at a neighbour's farm.

The first time a train rumbled by, I feared for my life. I had no idea what this horrible, clattering thing was.

More and more trains puffed and shrieked past the meadow.

12

John never mistreated me. James, the stable boy, was also kind. I had a good life at Birtwick Park.

Ginger and I learned to get along and made a good team as we worked.

Merrylegs, Ginger, and I became good friends.

19

On one exciting night, the stable bell woke me up. John and Joe rushed to put my saddle on.

Fasten this, Joe.

Hurry, John!

John rode me into town.

Doctor White, Mrs. Gordon is ill.

I'll need to ride your horse.

Black Beauty is tired, but he'll go until he drops.

The mistress was soon feeling better, but the doctor said she was still sick. He told her that she had to move somewhere warmer and better for her health.

A little while later, we took the Gordons to the train station.

And so we left our master and mistress. Then we slowly headed back to Birtwick Park, but it was not our home anymore.

Merrylegs had been given to Mr. Blomefield. Ginger and I had been sold to another farm.

27

John took us to our new home at Earlshall Park. Mr. York was our new coachman.

What can you tell me about these two?

There's not a better pair of horses anywhere.

Black Beauty has a perfect temper.

Ginger was treated poorly as a filly, but she behaves well when treated well.

31

I suffered with that rein for four months.
My neck and chest ached. My mouth and
tongue were always sore.

In my old home, John, Joe, and Squire Gordon
were my friends. And I had Merrylegs and
Ginger. Here, I didn't have any friends.

In the spring, our master went to London. He took York with him and left Reuben Smith in charge of the stables. Smith was a good horseman and always very gentle, until one strange day in town . . .

Along the way, I felt my shoe slip off.

There's a loose nail in your horse's front shoe.

Bah! He can make it home all right!

Stones on the road split my shoeless hoof.

Faster! Faster!

Other drivers thought horses were like steam engines and could pull heavy loads through any kind of weather.

I was up for sale again and again, and one day I was being sold at a horse fair.

Annual Horse Fair

41

Jerry had a cab of his own. I pulled it with a proud old horse, Captain. He had belonged to a soldier who had fought in the war.

Soon after, Jerry showed me off at the cab stand.

I don't know. I'd say he's worth whatever you paid, Jerry.

He looks too nice for the price you paid. You'll find something wrong with him.

The winter came that year, with a great deal of cold, wet weather.

The slippery streets were scary.

Easy does it.

48

49

One day, a shabby old cab with an old chestnut-coloured horse drove up beside ours.

Black Beauty, is that you?

Oh, my! Is that you, Ginger?

Yes. I have been sold many times, and each master has been worse than the last.

I now work for a man with a cab. He knows I am weak, so he is trying to get all he can out of me.

With a tug from her driver, Ginger drove off.

Farewell, Black Beauty.

54

The ladies decided to keep me.

I have now lived in this happy place a whole year. They call me by my old name: Black Beauty.

About Anna Sewell

Anna Sewell was born in 1820 in Norfolk, England. Around the age of 14, Sewell fell and injured her ankles. They didn't heal properly. From then on, she had trouble walking and relied on horses to take her where she needed to go. She loved horses and was grateful for them. Sewell was shocked to see how cruelly some people treated her favourite animal.

In 1871, Sewell was told she had only a short time to live. She decided to write a book that would show the kind and loving nature of horses. That book, the only one she ever wrote, was *Black Beauty*. It has been considered a classic since it was published in 1877.

About the Author

L. L. Owens was born in Iowa and now lives in Seattle, USA, with her husband. She has written more than 45 books, and she enjoys visiting classrooms to talk about her writing. She likes listening to music, cooking, and exploring the Pacific Northwest of the United States.

About the Illustrator

When she was younger, Jennifer Tanner loved to draw humorous comics about dogs who went on spectacular adventures through time and space, meeting alien creatures along the way. Today she spends her time illustrating many comic book stories.

GLOSSARY

colts (KOLTS) — young male horses

damaged (DAM-ijd) — broken or unable to heal

Duchess (DUTCH-iss) — the name of Black Beauty's mother, who was named for a duchess, the wife of a duke

filly (FILL-ee) — a young female horse

ignore (igg-NOR) — to not notice something or pretend that something didn't happen

lord (LORD) — a person who had a royal birth or had power over others

scolded (SKOLD-id) — told someone that they did something wrong, often in a mean way

squire (SKWIRE) — a country gentleman

stall (STAWL) — a section in a stable or barn where an animal is kept

THE LIFE OF A HORSE IN VICTORIAN TIMES

Black Beauty takes place in the mid-1800s, at a time when people used horses for transportation. Cars were not yet invented, and roads were often rough dirt tracks. The nicest roads were made of stones.

Horses wore **horseshoes** to protect their hooves. They usually wore a **saddle** on their backs and headgear called a **bridle**. The bridle has a **bit** that goes into the horse's mouth, and it is attached to the **reins**. The rider pulls on the reins to give signals to the horse. In the story, Black Beauty had to wear a **checkrein**. This is a short rein that keeps the horse's head high. Black Beauty also wore leather flaps called **blinders** on his bridle. They shielded his eyes, making him look straight ahead.

There are different titles for people who handle horses. The **groom** takes care of the horse in its stable. For fine carriages, which hold a few people, a **coachman** steers the horses. For a quick, short ride, people might ride in a cab. This is a small and less fancy carriage driven by a **cabbie**.

DISCUSSION QUESTIONS

1. Black Beauty's mother, Duchess, taught her son good manners. What are some good manners that you should use every day?

2. When he saw a dead horse in a cart, Black Beauty said he hoped that it was Ginger. Why did Black Beauty want Ginger to die?

3. Why did Lady York want Ginger and Black Beauty to wear the checkrein? Do you think that she treated the animals kindly?

4. At the end of the story, Black Beauty is called by his old name. Why does this make him feel happy?

WRITING PROMPTS

1. Towards the end of the story, Black Beauty thinks about Merrylegs and Ginger, his best friends. Describe each of the horses. What did they look like? How did they act?

2. Which place in the story do you think was Black Beauty's favourite? Describe your own favourite place and explain why it is your favourite.

3. Write a story about an animal in your life. What does the animal like? What does it dislike? What makes it sad or afraid? What makes it happy?

Other Books

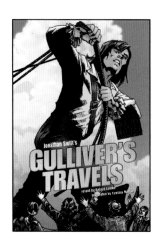

Gulliver's Travels

Lemuel Gulliver always dreamed of sailing across seas, but he never could have imagined the places his travels would take him. On the island of Lilliput, he is captured by tiny creatures no more than six inches tall. In a country of Blefuscu, he is nearly squashed by an army of giants. His adventures could be the greatest tales ever told, if he survives long enough to tell them.

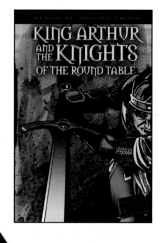

King Arthur and the Knights of the Round Table

In a world of wizards, giants, and dragons, King Arthur and the Knights of the Round Table are the kingdom of Camelot's only defence against the threatening forces of evil. Fighting battles and saving those in need, the Knights of the Round Table can defeat every enemy but one — themselves!

ROBIN HOOD

Robin Hood and his Merrie Men are the heroes of Sherwood Forest. Taking from the rich and giving to the poor, Robin Hood and his loyal followers fight for the downtrodden and oppressed. As they outwit the cruel Sheriff of Nottingham, Robin Hood and his Merrie Men are led on a series of exciting adventures.

TREASURE ISLAND

Jim Hawkins had no idea what he was getting into when the pirate Billy Bones showed up at the doorstep of his mother's inn. When Billy dies suddenly, Jim is left to unlock his old sea chest, which reveals money, a journal, and a treasure map. Joined by a band of honourable men, Jim sets sail on a dangerous voyage to locate the loot on a faraway island. The violent sea is only one of the dangers they face. They soon encounter a band of bloodthirsty pirates determined to make the treasure their own!

GRAPHIC REVOLVE

If you have enjoyed this story, there are many more exciting tales for you to discover in the Graphic Revolve collection...

20,000 Leagues Under the Sea

Black Beauty

Dracula

Frankenstein

Gulliver's Travels

The Hound of the Baskervilles

The Hunchback of Notre Dame

King Arthur and the Knights of the Round Table

Robin Hood

The Strange Case of Dr Jekyll and Mr Hyde

Treasure Island

The War of the Worlds